Foundations of Discipleship Training

Call to Awaken the Laity **Discipleship Training Vol.1**

Foundations of Discipleship Training

Copyright©2005, 2008 by John H. Oak

Published by DMI Press
1443-26 Seocho-1dong, Seocho-ku, Seoul 137-865, Korea

Printed in Seoul, Korea

ISBN 89-5731-084-3 03230

Visit our Web Site : www.discipleN.com

Call to Awaken the Laity **Discipleship Training 1**

Foundations of Discipleship Training

John H. Oak

ЮJ DMI

Why is Discipleship Training necessary?

Discipleship training is rooted in the words of Jesus Christ to His disciples in Matthew 28:18~20.

"Then Jesus came to them and said, All authority in heaven and on earth has been given to me. Therefore go and make disciples of all nations, baptizing them in the name of the Father and of the Son and of the Holy Spirit, and teaching them to obey everything I have commanded you. And surely I am with you always, to the very end of the age."

It is Jesus Christ, who holds all authority over the universe, who commanded us to make disciples of every nation. And disciples are to be made from every nation.

Therefore, the church must carry out discipleship training. The contents of Discipleship Training are the teachings of Jesus Christ. The key to Discipleship Training is obedience. The leader is responsible not only for teaching, but for obedience as well.

Who is qualified to train disciples? First and foremost, he must be a disciple himself. Jesus Himself entrusted this mission to the disciples whom He had taught and trained for three years.

It is very important to understand Jesus' intentions in telling His disciples not just to evangelize but to make disciples. If one understands why Jesus dedicated three years pouring forth all His energy into making only a few hand-picked disciples, it is not so difficult to understand His intention. Jesus was searching for those who would take on the responsibility of carrying out the work of saving the world and establishing the kingdom of God. And it would begin with only a few and not many. Jesus was convinced of Isaiah's prophecy, "The least of you will become a thousand, the smallest a mighty nation" (Isaiah 60:22). Jesus did not doubt that those few who were personally molded by Him would lead many and also conquer the world.

Therefore, Discipleship Training is a strategy to train a chosen few. It is a strategy to move many with a few. Behind the command of Jesus to make disciples was this hidden agenda. In the end, His decision proved right. Despite the meager beginning with the Twelve, the kingdom of God is soaring high in the world today through the countless number of disciples who continued after them - like the mighty water covering the ocean.

For a long time the church did not grasp the true significance behind Jesus' command to make disciples. The command was understood as a general command to evangelize. However a new understanding and challenge of Discipleship Training began through mission organizations that were stirring young people into radical dedication of their lives for the gospel. Over the years it has been proven that these organizations were right.

Now the huge task remains for local churches to take up the baton from mission organizations and train disciples. This undertaking is still in its infancy and has many obstacles to overcome.

Sarang Community Church has emphasized the vision of Discipleship Training since its founding years. This emphasis has been due to the firm belief that the church must produce Christ's disciples. Sarang Community Church has also been aware of the danger that the church will be unfit to deal with contemporary society unless those who attend church become disciples of Christ.

Mobilizing the entire church by focusing on a few individuals at a time has been carried out through Discipleship Training. Though it has been a difficult road, Sarang Community Church has been able to bear much fruit with God's blessings during the past twenty or more years. It is a joy to see an increasing number of churches sending the message that discipleship is possible.

Those who have undergone Discipleship Training can serve one another according to their gifts and thus play a lead role in creating organic fellowship within the church. Through the service of teaching and building up fellow believers, the entire church emerges as disciples of Christ before the world. I am convinced that this is the shortcut for the church to fulfill its calling as the salt and light of the world.

Discipleship Training is achieved in a small group environment. It is also shaped by the pastor. This is the model and a guide to leadership that Jesus has shown us.

The church must recover its essence and calling in order to renew its members and rejuvenate its image. This is possible only when the church firmly establishes its identity as both the people of God called from the world and the disciples of Christ sent to the world. Discipleship Training is the most biblical and effective way to awaken the laity to their identity and calling. I have no doubt that before long a new chapter will open where all churches will be transformed into disciples of Christ. As written in Matthew 19:26, it is impossible with man but possible with God. Then Jesus Christ, the Lord of all, will receive all the glory and praise.

Points to Consider

The following points should be kept in order to complete
Discipleship Training successfully.

1. In order to benefit fully from the training, you should love and trust your leader and pray for him/her faithfully.

2. Go to every meeting and complete the training. Members might face one or two crisis during the training, but every member should help and care for each other to overcome the crisis.

3. Prepare for each lesson. Your preparation makes a big difference to your training.

4. Do the weekly homework. Develop from the beginning a habit of doing your homework thoroughly and regularly.

5. This is an opportunity to train the whole person. A person who only uses his or her head might well become a cold theorist, but cannot become a disciple who loves Jesus. All of our mind, emotion, and will must be involved in order to experience the wonderful intervention of the Holy Spirit. Have you learned the Word? Then embrace the Word and pray. Prayer is putting what you have learned into your heart. Then immediately apply the Word to your daily life. You will discover that you are becoming more like Christ as you learn, understand, and put the Word into practice. "Oh, how I love your law! I meditate on it all day long" (Psalms 119:97).

Contents

Foundation of Discipleship Training

In the first book, we will learn the basic training patterns that we must practice daily. We will learn how to daily read the Word and pray.

We should not forget even for a moment that keeping up an intimate fellowship with God by the daily reading of the word and prayer has a deciding effect on our discipleship training and spiritual growth.

1

My Testimony and Confession of Faith

If you believe in Jesus, you should be able to give your testimony of faith wherever you are and to whomever you meet. Believers in the first century proudly shared their faith in Jesus Christ with their families and gave their testimonies at their work places without being ashamed - even though they could have been put to death for admitting that they were Christians. It's a tragedy of our modern age when those attending church are either ashamed of professing their faith or, worse yet, do not have assurance of their own salvation. It is only within an environment of sharing each another's faith and testimonies that we can experience a deep spiritual fellowship that engages both our minds and our hearts. The disappearance of that kind of fellowship is one of the reasons for the coldness that the church is experiencing today. We are all new to this meeting and are here to begin the journey of discipleship together. It is very important that we open our hearts and accept one another. So now let's honestly profess our faith and listen closely to the testimonies of our brothers and sisters. The joy that can be experienced in the presence of God's children will enrich our hearts.

1. Paul enjoyed giving an account of how he met Jesus Christ whenever he felt it would help in the preaching of the Gospel. Read Acts 22:1-16 carefully. What are the three elements of Paul's testimony?

_____

_____

_____

_____

_____

2. First, Paul honestly describes the kind of person he was before he met Christ. What kind of person was he? (vv. 3-5)

_____

_____

_____

_____

_____

3. Next, Paul gives a vivid description of how he met Christ. Summarize the content (vv. 6-10).

_____

_____

_____

_____

_____

4. Last, he describes the person he became after his conversion. What kind of person did he become? (vv. 13-15)

5. From Paul's testimony, we learn that there are at least three points that should be included in our testimonies: our circumstances before we believed in Christ, the process of coming to trust in Jesus, and the changes that took place after encountering Him. Can you present your testimony in this manner? Write down and then give your testimony.

6. There is one important point missing in Paul's testimony as we studied it. Find the missing point by comparing Paul's testimony with Peter's in Matthew 16:16-17.

15

7. Can you confess that Jesus is your Savior? Using your own words, clearly articulate your confession of faith in Christ.

_____

_____

_____

_____

8. If you find it difficult to give a testimony with confidence like Paul and Peter did, what do you think are the reasons?

_____

_____

_____

_____

9. Occasionally we meet Christians enthusiastically sharing their testimony. They usually have had some incredible experience at conversion or a dramatic change in their life since coming to Jesus. On the other hand, those born into a Christian family or who have gone to Sunday school ever since they were little children sometimes seem hesitant about giving their testimonies. In which group do you find yourself?

_____

_____

_____

10. Whether or not we have had a dramatic experience, it is still our duty to profess Jesus Christ as our Savior before other people. The important thing is that we confess our faith with conviction. During this lesson, you have heard the testimonies of your brothers and sisters and have probably found some reasons behind the problems you face in sharing your testimony. Write down your confession of faith in the form of a testimonial and bring it with you next week.

② A Daily Encounter with God

We must recognize that 'believing in Jesus' and 'sharing our heart in communion with God' are not the same. From time to time, we see people who build walls in their relationship with their parents. This is a good illustration of the fact that being born as someone's child does not guarantee a good relationship with one's parents. The same idea applies to our relationship with God our Father. In order to maintain a healthy and joyous spiritual life, we must be faithful in sharing our heart with God in spiritual fellowship with Him. We refer to this daily communion with God as having a quiet time (QT). When we form the habit of each day setting aside a certain time to praise, read His Word, and pray, we will be able to enjoy the blessings of God. We will be like a branch that receives nourishment from the tree and whose leaves turn green and produce fruit. It is very important to form this valuable habits in the early stage of discipleship training. Without this kind of daily spiritual fellowship, it is impossible to do great things for the glory of God. Fellowship between friends becomes joyous and sweet when it is naturally and continuously maintained. We should be able to experience this sweetness in our relationship with God as well. Now let's study how to have this kind of communion with God on a daily basis.

1. The author of Hebrews eloquently describes the meaning of 'having fellowship with God.' Refer to Hebrews 4:16 and answer the following questions.

a) When do we need fellowship?

_____

_____

_____

_____

_____

b) What is the purpose of having fellowship?

_____

_____

_____

_____

_____

c) Where should we go in order to have fellowship with God?

_____

_____

_____

_____

_____

2. Jesus maintained wonderful fellowship with God while He was in the world. Explain where and when Jesus had fellowship with God (Mark 1:35).

_____

_____

_____

_____

_____

_____

3. Jesus' daily life was extremely busy. From Mark 1, let us trace through how Jesus spent twenty-four hours from the day of Sabbath to the following day.

a) The Sabbath morning (vv. 21-28)

_____

_____

_____

_____

_____

b) The Sabbath afternoon (vv. 29-31)

_____

_____

_____

_____

_____

c) The Sabbath evening (vv. 32-34)

_____

_____

_____

_____

_____

_____

d) The following morning (v. 35)

_____

_____

_____

_____

_____

4. How do you feel when you consider that Jesus spent time with God early in the morning despite His busy schedule?

_____

_____

_____

_____

_____

_____

_____

_____

5. Do you have a habit of skipping quiet time by making excuses such as 'I am too busy' or 'don't have time'? If you do, explain when you started to skip QT and the damage it has had on your spiritual life.

6. Why do you think it is difficult to set aside a time for God to meet with Him daily even when you desire to do so?

7. Is there any habit you should form in order to be faithful in having quiet times?

8. We can learn from Jesus that prayer is necessary in order to have proper fellowship with God. How is your daily prayer life?

_____

_____

_____

_____

_____

9. To read and meditate upon the Word is to listen attentively to His voice in our daily encounter with God. Read Psalm 119:97-102 and answer the following questions.

a) What should be our attitude toward the Bible? (v. 97)

_____

_____

_____

b) What should be our attitude toward reading and studying the Bible? (v. 102)

_____

_____

_____

c) How do we cherish the Word that we have learned? (vv. 97, 99)

_____

_____

_____

d) How do we live according to the Word we have learned? (v. 101)

_____

_____

_____

10. Among the above two elements, which is most difficult for you?

_____

_____

_____

_____

11. Review what you have learned in this lesson and share with others if there is anything you need to put into action immediately.

_____

_____

_____

_____

I promise to meet with God

From (:   ) to (:   )

_____ (Year) _____ (Month) _____ (Day)

_____ (Signature)

③ Quiet Time

Last week we learned that a successful Christian life requires a daily meeting with God. Quiet time is having communion with God through praying and reading the Bible. Now the remaining, much needed subject is to consider how to go about having that daily quiet time. Over the past century, Korean churches have been holding dawn prayer services, after which people have individual prayer time and reading of the Word. One can have marvelous fellowship with God this way. Recently there has been a growing interest in a more direct approach in which lay people pray and meditate on the Word on their own rather than just passively attend services led by a pastor. Nowadays, various ways of having effective quiet time are being made available. We will introduce a few in this lesson. Try to put into practice one of the methods recommended by your leader.

1. Share with the group how you spent time with God during the past week and the blessings you received.

_____

_____

_____

_____

2. Meditation on the Word can be divided into the following four steps. The following example is a quiet time note written by a sister who was receiving discipleship training. Read carefully and observe the differences between each step.

Title: A person who serves (Luke 22:24~27)	
Observation	The disciples were arguing about who is greater. Jesus spoke and said, 'The kings of the Gentiles lord it over them; and those who exercise authority over them call themselves Benefactors. But you are not to be like that. Instead, the greatest among you should be like the youngest, and the one who rules like the one who serves. For who is greater, the one who is at the table or the one who serves? Is it not the one who is at the table? But I am among you as one who serves.'
Investigation and Meditation	The disciples did not understand what was on Jesus' heart. Jesus had spoken of the suffering He was about to undergo and of the one who would betray Him as He shared the bread and wine with the disciples before the dispute arose. Even in such sorrowful and solemn circumstances, the disciples were filled with selfish concern about their own position instead of being concerned about what was on Jesus' heart. The disciples were feuding over the issue of 'Who is the greatest.' Their struggle was not new. A sad example is the incident in

Investigation and Meditation

which the two sons of Zebedee asked Jesus, with cunning antici-
pation, for permission to sit at the right and left hands of Jesus
(Mark 10:37). The other disciples who heard this were very upset
and became indignant (Mark 10:41).

They should have borne in their minds Jesus' teaching and example. Only a few days ago when the disciples caused trouble over
the same issue, Jesus had given them an important lesson, 'and
whoever wants to be first must be a slave to all' (Mark 10:43-44).
And Jesus said that He came to serve although He is their teacher
(Mark 10:45). Why did they forget this lesson so quickly?

Reflection

There is always a struggle in my heart as well because of this
desire to be great. I personally like to be the best and the first,
and I am also filled with ambition to be recognized by others
through my husband and children. However, true greatness
comes from being acknowledged by God rather than by the
world. But how I have tried to attain recognition from both God
and man! The principle of the kingdom of God - that to lower one-
self is to be exalted - differs from the principle of the world. And I
have realized that trying to attain both the principle of God's kingdom and the principle of the world is impossible.

Application

When I first started discipleship training, my focus was to do my
best and be the best. However, as I studied with my fellow sisters
for the past few months, that pride has begun to subside. I saw
that my fellow sisters were purer, more passionate, and steadier,
and their desire to be transformed in the Lord was great. Through
them, I came to see my pride and ambition and repented of
them. Now I am trying to learn from their purity, and take delight
in being challenged by them. I would like to put a few things into
practice this week to live as a servant.

Help my small group leader – I will prepare a dish for my small
group leader who is physically weak and is concerned about the
following week's study.

Our small group has decided to prepare lunch for the sports tour-
nament on Oct. 1. I now feel guilty that I had planned to say that I
don't have time and take on a lighter responsibility. I will prepare
wholeheartedly and with sincerity.

3. If you were to record your quiet time in this fashion, which would you find to be most difficult and which most doable among the four stages?

_____

_____

_____

_____

_____

4. A quiet time note is generally arranged in the following format. Use the table for comparison.

Method	Observation	Meditation & Investigation	Reflection	Application
A			O	
B	O		O	
C	O		O	O
D	O	O	O	O

5. Among the four types - A, B, C, and D - which type do you prefer?

_____

_____

_____

_____

_____

6. Using the passage selected by your leader, record a quiet time note using the format you find most suitable for you. Afterwards share your note with others in the group.

The Living and Active Word of God

All books in the world eventually become lifeless with the passing of time. Even a classic masterpiece, at best, remains only partially true and slightly inspirational. In comparison, the Bible transcends the bounds of time and remains the living Word. Not only does the Bible itself witness to this fact, but there are countless instances from the real world that also testify to this fact. If we do not fully grasp the imperishable truth of the Bible, we grievously misunderstand God's Word and power just like the Sadducees and Pharisees of New Testament times. Let us reaffirm that the Word of God is living and active. What a wonderful discovery and blessing this is!

1. How does Hebrews 4:12-13 describe the Bible?

_____

_____

_____

_____

2. There are two purposes that God had in giving us His living word in a written form. What are they?

   • 2 Timothy 3:15

_____

_____

_____

_____

   • 2 Timothy 3:16-17

_____

_____

_____

_____

3. Whether or not the Bible is indeed the living word of God can be seen in the power of the Gospel to save sinners. How does Romans 1:16 explain this?

_____

_____

_____

_____

4. When did you realize that the Bible is the power of God for salvation?

_____

_____

_____

_____

_____

_____

5. The second purpose in giving us the Bible was to make each one of us into a whole person whose character and life reflect God's design. In this context, what does it mean to be made whole? (Ephesians 4:14-16)

_____

_____

_____

_____

_____

6. What does it mean to become whole to do good works? (Ephesians 4:19-24)

_____

_____

_____

_____

_____

_____

7. We must not misinterpret "being made whole." It does not mean that we do not sin nor that we live in a flawless, perfect state. Rather, being made whole refers to the sanctification process in which the children of God become more like Christ each day. Therefore, the importance lies in the degree to which we are being made whole as we read and study the word of God each day. What does 1 John 3:3 teach us with respect to this point?

8. In comparison to the person you were a year ago, to what extent have you been made 'whole'? Please give one or two specific examples.

9. What are the four amazing functions of the Bible that make us whole? (2 Timothy 3:16)

10. 'Teaching' instructs us about good and evil. 'Rebuking' points out our sins. 'Correcting' causes us to repent. 'Training in righteousness' leads us to walk according to the truth.

11. There are too many people around us who carry their Bible religiously, and yet experience no change in their life. They cannot accept rebuke even when they read the Bible. They don't want to repent. They are not able to discern truth. Nevertheless they consider this a trivial matter. What an oppressive thought! Close your eyes and examine yourself and your own life.

(5) What is a Proper Prayer?

There is nothing more influential in the life of God's children than a consistent prayer life through which we approach God's throne. Someone referred to prayer as 'breathing' for the soul. This poignantly expresses the importance of prayer. As we cannot live without breathing, our spiritual life cannot be sustained without prayer. Gordon gives us heart-striking advice in the following words:

"The great people of the earth to-day are the people who pray. I do not mean those who talk about prayer; nor those who say they believe in prayer; nor yet those who can explain about prayer; but I mean these people who take time and pray. They have not time. It must be taken from something else. This something else is important. Very important, and pressing than prayer. There are people that put prayer first, and group the other items in life's schedule around and after prayer." [1]

---

1) S.D. Gordon, *Quiet Talks on Prayer*

1. Read Hebrews 4:14-16 at least 5 times. Memorize verse 16. Summarize the passage.

   _____

   _____

   _____

2. Jesus is our 'Great High Priest'. Where does He presently reside? (v. 16)

   _____

   _____

   _____

   _____

3. Notice the word 'then' or 'therefore' in verse 16. This is a good ground for us to hold onto Jesus in prayer. After examining verses 15 and 16 in conjunction, explain why this is so.

   _____

   _____

   _____

   _____

4. Prayer is indeed a great privilege of going to the 'Great High Priest.' Have you taken for granted or neglected this great privilege and thus became a foolish and poor person?

   _____

   _____

   _____

   _____

5. There are many pitfalls we need to avoid when we pray. First of all, what warning did Jesus give from the example of the Pharisees' prayer? (Matthew 6:5)

_____

_____

_____

_____

_____

6. What kind of prayer does God delight in? (Matthew 6:6-7)

_____

_____

_____

_____

_____

7. What is 'room' referring to? Can you describe your 'room'?

_____

_____

_____

_____

_____

8. What do you think 'babbling like pagans' or 'heaping up empty phrases' mean?

_____

_____

_____

_____

9. Have you ever uttered thoughtless and empty words in your prayer? Give examples of prayer in which it is easy to babble or utter empty words.

_____

_____

_____

_____

_____

10. The Lord's Prayer teaches us what we should seek when we pray. Let's look at Matthew 6:9-13 and observe the priorities of prayer.

- Three things we should seek first for the glory of God

_____

_____

_____

_____

_____

- Four things we should seek next for our needs

_____

_____

_____

_____

_____

11. What is the utmost concern in your prayer? In other words what is the most important thing that you seek when you pray?

_____

_____

_____

_____

_____

_____

12. Compare your prayer concerns with the concerns taught by Jesus.

_____

_____

_____

_____

_____

_____

13. Do you feel a need to modify your prayers now that you have studied the prayer that Jesus taught? If so, how would you modify them?

_____

_____

_____

_____

_____

_____

_____

6

Answers to Prayer

"How many times have your prayers been answered?" If you were asked that, how many instances of answered prayers would you be able to give with confidence? Surprisingly, many people do not receive answers to their prayers even though they often pray. Jesus repeatedly made the promise in the Bible that prayer will be answered. The fact that the promise was repeated many times indicates the seriousness of the promise. If our prayers are not answered even when we pray for the right things, it does a disservice to the glory of God. Therefore, if there is no answer to a prayer, the problem lies within us. God's promises are not powerless. God answers our prayers, however, He sometimes gives us what He wants to give even though we may not be satisfied with it.

1. Read Matthew 7:7-11 to find out how Jesus explained answers to prayers. How many verses of Matthew 7:7-11 do you know by heart?

_____

_____

_____

_____

_____

_____

2. Pay close attention to the different metaphors Jesus used to establish the certainty of the promise that prayers will be answered (vv. 7-8).

_____

_____

_____

_____

_____

_____

3. God compares Himself to an earthly father in verses 9-11. There is a promise that God repeatedly pledges by using two metaphoric examples. What is that promise?

_____

_____

_____

_____

_____

_____

4. We have the habit of doubting God despite such an assuring promise. How do you feel about this promise?

_____

_____

_____

_____

_____

5. If you have accepted the promise in verse 11 without any reservations, you should feel an impulse to run to God and lay down all that is in your heart before Him. How much of such an urge do you feel rising in your heart?

_____

_____

_____

_____

_____

_____

6. Examine the following passages and find out some of the obstacles that can prevent our prayers from being answered.

   • Isaiah 1:15

_____

_____

_____

• Matthew 6:14-15

• James 1:6-7 (See also Matthew 11:24)

• James 4:3

7. Moses taught us a way to receive speedy answers to our prayers. First, read Exodus 32:7-8. Why was God angry? Then read verses 11-13 and examine the earnest plea that Moses made on behalf of the Israelites.

8. Next, pay close attention to how swiftly God answered the prayer (v. 14).

_____

_____

_____

_____

9. Moses was able to have his prayer answered promptly because he held on to and claimed the promise that God gave to the forefathers, "⋯ to whom you swore by your own self" (v. 13). Why does God answer our prayers quickly when we claim His promises in our prayers?

_____

_____

_____

_____

_____

10. How often do you go before God in prayer claiming His promises in order to receive answers? Give an example of a promise of God that you held onto and the answer you received.

_____

_____

_____

_____

11. Answers to prayer do not always come over night. Needless to say there are times when answers do come within an hour or two. However, often answers are given over a period of time as we continue to pray without despairing. Describe experience when your prayer was answered after praying over an extended period of time.

_____

_____

_____

_____

_____

12. Compare your prayer life with the prayer life of other members of your group, and see if there is any aspect in your prayer life that needs to change.

_____

_____

_____

_____

_____

Appendix

Bible Reading Guide

week	period	Training Discipleship	Training Ministry	day 1	day 2	day 3	day 4	day 5	day 6	day 7
1		Orientation		Gen 1~2	3~5	6~9	10~11	12~14	15~17	18~20
2		1-1	1-1	21~24	25~26	27~31	32~36	37~40	41~44	45~47
3		1-2	1-2	48~50	Mt 1~4	5~7	8~11	12~15	16~19	20~23
4		1-3	1-3	24~25	26~28	Ex 1~2	3~6	7~10	11~12	13~15
5		1-4	1-4	16~18	19~20	21~24	25~27	28~31	32~34	35~40
6		1 5	1-5	Mk 1~3	4~7	8~10	11~13	14~16	Lev 1~3	4~7
7		1-6	1-6	8~10	11~15	16~17	18~20	21~23	24~27	Lk 1~2
8		2-1	2-1	3~6	7~9	10~12	13~15	16~18	19~21	22~24
9	semester I	2-2	2-2	Nu 1~4	5~8	9~12	13~16	17~20	21~25	26~30
10		2-3	2-3	31~33	34~36	Jn 1~2	3~5	6~8	9~12	13~17
11		2-4	2-4	18~21	Dt 1~4	5~7	8~11	12~16	17~20	21~26
12		2-5	2-5	27~30	31~34	Jos 1~5	6~8	9~12	13~17	18~21
13		2-6	2-6	22~24	Jdg 1~5	6~8	9~12	13~16	17~21	Ru 1~4
14		2-7	2-7	Ac 1~4	5~7	8~9	10~12	13~15	16~18	19~20
15		2-8	2-8	21~23	24~26	27~28	1Sa 1~3	4~8	9~12	13~15
16		2-9	2-9	16~19	20~23	24~26	27~31	2Sa 1~4	5~7	8~10
17		2-10	3-1	11~14	15~18	19~20	21~24	Ro 1~3	4~5	6~8
18		2-11	3-2	9~11	12~16	1Ki 1~4	5~8	9~11	12~16	17~19
19		2-12	3-3	20~23	2Ki 1~3	4~8	9~12	13~17	18~21	22~25
20		2-13	3-4	1Ch 1~9	10~16	17~21	22~27	28~29	2Ch 1~5	6~9
21		2-14	3-5	10~12	13~16	17~20	21~25	26~28	29~32	33~36
22	vacation (Vac)	Vac-1	Vac-1	1Co 1~6	7~10	11~14	15~16	Ezr 1~3	4~6	Ezr 7~10 / 2Co 1~9
23		Vac-2	Vac-2	2Co 10~13	Ne 1~2	3~4	5~7	8~10	Ne 11~13	Gal 1~6 / Est 1~7
24		Vac-3	Vac-3	Est 8~10	Job 1~3	4~7	8~10	11~14	15~17	Job 18~28
25		Vac-4	Vac-4	Job 29~31	32~34	35~37	38~39	40~42	Ps 1~6	Ps 7~30
26		Vac-5	Vac-5	Ps 31~36	37~41	42~49	50~54	55~59	60~66	67~89
27		Vac-6	Vac-6	Ps 90~97	98~103	104~106	107~110	111~118	119	Ps 120~145
28		Vac-7	Vac-7	Ps 146~150	Pr 1~4	5~9	10~13	14~17	18~21	Pr 22~31 / Ecc 1~6
29		Vac-8	Vac-8	Ecc 7~12	Ss 1~8	Eph 1~6	Isa 1~4	5~7	8~12	13~20
30		Vac-9	Vac-9	Isa 21~23	24~27	28~30	31~35	36~39	40~43	44~48
31	semester II	3-1	3-6	Isa 49~51	52~57	58~62	63~66	Php 1~4	Jer 1~3	4~6
32		3-2	3-7	7~10	11~15	16~20	21~25	26~29	30~33	34~39
33		3-3	3-8	40~45	46~49	50~52	Col 1~4	La 1~5	1Th 1~5	Eze 1~6
34		3-4	3-9	7~11	12~15	16~19	20~23	24~28	29~32	33~36
35		3-5	4-1	37~39	40~43	44~48	2Th 1~3	Da 1~3	4~6	7~12
36		3-6	4-2	1Ti 1~6	Hos 1~3	4~6	7~8	9~11	12~14	2Ti 1~4
37		3-7	4-3	Joe 1~3	Tit 1~3	Am 1~2	3~5	6~7	8~9	Phm
38		3-8	4-4	Ob	Heb 1~2	3~4	5~7	8~10	11~13	Jnh 1~4
39		3-9	4-5	Jas 1~5	Mic 1~2	3~5	6~7	1Pe 1~5	Na 1~3	2Pe 1~3
40		3-10	4-6	Hab 1~3	1Jn 1~5	Zep 1~3	2Jn	Hag 1~2	3Jn	Zec 1~2
41		3-11	Lecture I	3~4	5~6	7~8	9~11	12~14	Jude	Mal 1~4
42		3-12	Lecture II	Rev 1~3	4~6	7~9	10~13	14~16	17~19	20~22

Bible Memory Verses

Theme	Wk.	Title	Bible Verse 1	Bible Verse 2
Foundations of Discipleship Training	1	My Testimony and Confession of Faith	Rom 10:9~10	Matt 16:16
	2	A Daily Encounter with God	Heb 4:16	La 3:22~23
	3	Quiet Time	Psalms 1:1~2	Psalms 119:105
	4	The Living and Active Word of God	Rom 1:16	2 Tim 3:16
	5	What is a Proper Prayer?	Phil 4:6~7	Matt 6:6
	6	Answers to Prayer	John 15:7	Matt 7:11
My Unshakable Salvation	7	The Authority of the Bible	2 Peter 1:21	Joshua 1:8
	8	Who is God?	Rom 11:36a	Jer 31:3b
	9	Who is Jesus Christ?	Heb 4:15	John 14:6
	10	The Trinity	John 1:1	2 Cor 13:13
	11	The Fall of Humanity and Its Results	Rom 5:12	Heb 9:27
	12	The Death of Jesus Christ	Rom 5:8	Gal 3:13
	13	The Resurrection of Jesus Christ	Rom 4:25	Gal 2:20
	14	The Coming of the Promised Holy Spirit	Acts 2:38	1 Cor 12:13
	15	Rebirth	Titus 3:5	1 Thess 1:3~4
	16	What is Faith?	Eph 2:8~9	Rom 4:18
	17	Righteousness through Grace	Rom 3:21~22	Rom 8:32
	18	The Holy Spirit in Us	Rom 8:26	Gal 5:22~23
	19	The Sanctification of Believers	2 Cor 7:1	1 John 3:3
	20	The Second Coming of Jesus Christ	Rev 22:7	1 Thess 4:16~17
Becoming Like Jesus	21	A Life of Obedience	Matt. 7:24	John 14:21
	22	A Responsibility to Serve	Phil 2:3~4	1 Peter 4:11a
	23	A Life that Testifies of Christ	Matt 28:19~20	Matt 5:16
	24	A Person of Edifying Speech	Luke 6:45	Pr 15:23
	25	Spiritual Growth and Maturity	Eph 4:13	Phil 3:12
	26	A Life of Purity	1 Cor 6:19~20	2 Tim 2:22
	27	Christian Family Life	Eph 6:1~3	Deut 6:6-7
	28	Trials and Spiritual Character	Psalms 119:71	Rom 8:28
	29	The Sovereignty of Christ	Rom 14:7~8	Rev 3:20
	30	Stewardship	Eph 5:15~16	1 Tim 6:17
	31	Spiritual Warfare	1 Peter 5:8	Eph 6:10~11
	32	A New Commandment: Love One Another	John 13:34~35	1 John 3:18

* The above Bible memory chart is from Navigators. Used by permission.

Self-Check Homework Chart

Name

Check by symbols   ∩ˑ All completed   △ˑ Partially completed   ×ˑ Incomplete

Date	Subject Matter	Preparation	QT	Memory Verse	Bible Reading	Special Project	Leader (Check the Work)